C000204901

THE GREAT BIBLE DISCOVERY

AFTER EASTER

THE BIBLE IS A BEST-SELLER. IT IS ALSO ONE OF THE MASTER-WORKS OF WORLD LITERATURE - SO IMPORTANT THAT UNIVERSITIES TODAY TEACH 'NON-RELIGIOUS' BIBLE COURSES TO HELP STUDENTS WHO CHOOSE TO STUDY WESTERN LITERATURE.

THE BIBLE POSSESSES AN AMAZING POWER TO FASCINATE YOUNG AND OLD ALIKE.

ONE REASON FOR THIS UNIVERSAL APPEAL IS THAT IT DEALS WITH BASIC HUMAN LONGINGS, EMOTIONS, RELATIONSHIPS. 'ALL THE WORLD IS HERE.' ANOTHER REASON IS THAT SO MUCH OF THE BIBLE CONSISTS OF STORIES. THEY ARE FULL OF MEANING BUT EASY TO REMEMBER.

HERE ARE THOSE STORIES, PRESENTED SIMPLY AND WITH A MINIMUM OF EXPLANATION. WE HAVE LEFT THE TEXT TO SPEAK FOR ITSELF. GIFTED ARTISTS USE THE ACTION-STRIP TECHNIQUE TO BRING THE BIBLE'S DEEP MESSAGE TO READERS OF ALL AGES. THEIR DRAWINGS ARE BASED ON INFORMATION FROM ARCHAEOLOGICAL DISCOVERIES COVERING FIFTEEN CENTURIES.

AN ANCIENT BOOK - PRESENTED FOR THE PEOPLE OF THE SECOND MILLENNIUM. A RELIGIOUS BOOK - PRESENTED FREE FROM THE INTERPRETATION OF ANY PARTICULAR CHURCH. A UNIVERSAL BOOK - PRESENTED IN A FORM THAT ALL MAY ENJOY.

M publishing
CARLISLE, UK

22

Jesus had told his disciples that death would not be the end for him. But the idea that he might rise from the dead was so far from their minds that they at first refused to believe that this had happened. Two things finally convinced them. (1) On the 'third day' the tomb was found empty. (Paul refers to this very early tradition in a letter written about AD 57 -1 Corinthians 15:3-4.) (2) Jesus appeared to them here and there, sharing food, talking with them and teaching them. After forty days these appearances suddenly ceased - unlike what would have been the case if it had been 'all imagination'.

Then as the Spirit of Jesus came to them at Pentecost, they were transformed and displayed courage and love like his. Led by Peter, they proclaimed in Jerusalem that Jesus was the messiah, challenging those who heard them to repent of having rejected him and to believe in him. Soon there was a large fellowship of Christ's disciples, baptized in his name. They worshipped in the Temple and in their own homes, they learned about Jesus from the apostles, they even shared their property.

The disciples had learned much from Jesus during his earthly life. Now the Holy Spirit enriched this knowledge. He helped them to realize Jesus was with them. He helped them to trust Jesus. He made them stronger people, more loving, more courageous. Ever since, Christians all over the world have had a similar experience.

Like many followers of Jesus today, the Jerusalem disciples were persecuted. But this had an unexpected result. Although Jesus had told his followers to spread the good news throughout the world, they shared the message at first only with their fellow-Jews. However, when the Jewish religious leaders began not only to imprison but even to kill members of the Jerusalem church, many of them took refuge in distant villages and towns.

And so these 'ordinary Christians' helped to spread the good news about Jesus the Saviour further and further.

MATTHEW 28
MARK 16
LUKE 24
JOHN 14-16; 20-21
ACTS 1-8

AFTER EASTER

22

First published as *Découvrir la Bible* 1983

First edition © Larousse S.A. 1984
24-volume series adaptation by Mike Jacklin © Knowledge Unlimited 1994
This edition © OM Publishing 1995

01 00 99 98 97 96 95   7 6 5 4 3 2 1

OM Publishing is an imprint of Send the Light Ltd.,
P.O. Box 300, Carlisle, Cumbria CA3 0QS, U.K.

Introductions: Peter Cousins

British Library Cataloguing in Publication Data
A catalogue record for this book is available from the British Library
ISBN 1-85078-226-1

Printed in Singapore by Tien Wah Press (Pte) Ltd.

N AS THE SABBATH ENDED,
OF MAGDALA, MARY THE MOTHER
MES AND JESUS, AND
E WENT TO THE TOMB TO
T THE BODY OF JESUS.
HE TOMB WAS OPEN, AND...

SOMEONE'S TAKEN THE LORD'S BODY AWAY!

WHOEVER WOULD DO SUCH A THING?

THE RISEN CHRIST

SCENARIO: Etienne DAHLER
DRAWING: Carlo MARCELLO

BUT... WHAT'S GOING ON HERE?

STAY HERE. I'M GOING TO TELL PETER.

I DON'T UNDERSTAND. THERE WERE GUARDS, WEREN'T THERE?

WHERE HAVE THEY GONE?

WHILE PETER AND JOHN WENT BACK TO THE UPPER ROOM...

...MARY OF MAGDALA WENT BACK TO THE TOMB...

MARY OF MAGDALA RAN TO THE UPPER ROOM TO TELL THE DISCIPLES THE NEWS. THOMAS WAS THERE TOO.

SOON THE OTHER WOMEN ARRIVED ...

EWS
LY
HED
HIGH
TS...

SPREAD THE RUMOUR THAT HIS DISCIPLES STOLE HIS BODY WHILE THE GUARDS WERE ASLEEP.

WHAT ELSE COULD HAVE HAPPENED?

THAT AFTERNOON, TWO DISCIPLES LEFT JERUSALEM, ON THE WAY TO EMMAUS...

LIFE GOES ON AS IF NOTHING'S HAPPENED!

ALL THE SAME, THE WOMEN'S STORIES TROUBLE ME.

SUS JOINED
EM ON THE ROAD,
T THEY DIDN'T
COGNIZE HIM.

WHAT ARE YOU TALKING ABOUT?

DON'T YOU KNOW WHAT'S JUST HAPPENED IN JERUSALEM?

WHAT?

JESUS... OF NAZARETH...

7

A POWERFUL PROPHET! OUR PRIESTS HANDED HIM OVER TO BE CRUCIFIED.

BUT WE'D BEEN HOPING HE'D DELIVER ISRAEL...

NOW THE WOMEN ARE CLAIMING THAT THEY SAW HIM ALIVE THIS MORNING!

HOW CAN WE BELIEVE A THING?

BUT THAT'S WHAT THE PRO... SAID WOULD HAPPEN...

THEY SAID THAT THE MESSIAH MUST SUFFER AND BE PUT TO DEATH BEFORE HE COULD ENTER INTO HIS GLORY!

THEN HE EXPLAINED EVERYTHING THE SCRIPTURES HAD TO SAY ABOUT HIMSELF.

AS THEY REACHED EMMAUS...

I'LL BE MOVING ON...

NO, STAY WITH US! THE DAY'S NEARLY OVER.

LET'S GO AND EA... AT THAT INN.

BLESS YOU, LORD, GOD OF THE UNIVERSE, FOR THIS BREAD, FRUIT OF THE EARTH!

AMEN!

AMEN!

TAKE SOME, AND EAT IT!

JESUS!

JESUS!

HE'S ALIVE!

THE WOMEN WERE TELLING THE TRUTH!

THEY HURRIED STRAIGHT BACK TO JERUSALEM.

THEY'LL NEVER BELIEVE US!

THE WELCOMED THEM INTO THE UPPER ROOM.

CLEOPAS, THE LORD'S RISEN! HE'S APPEARED TO SIMON PETER!

TO HIM TOO?

PETER, WE CAME SPECIALLY TO TELL YOU THAT WE MET HIM ON THE ROAD TO EMMAUS!

PRAISE THE LORD FOR SUCH WONDERFUL THINGS!

...SALEM WAS FULL OF RUMOURS.

...HEY'RE SPYING ON US. ...O MEN FOLLOWED ...E THIS MORNING.

IT'S NOT SAFE HERE ANY LONGER. LET'S GO BACK TO GALILEE.

ONE EVENING PETER DECIDED TO GO FISHING. BUT THAT NIGHT...

NOT A SINGLE FISH! JOHN, I'VE NEVER SEEN ANYTHING LIKE IT.

BUT, PETER, REMEMBER THE MARVELLOUS CATCH...

HEY, THERE! ...VE YOU CAUGHT ANYTHING?

NO!

...OW OUT THE NET ...THE RIGHT SIDE ...F THE BOAT!

HELP ME!

THE NET'S GOING TO BREAK!

PETER, IT'S THE LORD! I'M SURE IT IS!

PETER!

LET'S FOLLOW HIM IN THE BOAT.

11

BRING SOME OF THE FISH YOU'VE JUST CAUGHT.

NOW COME AND HAVE BREAKFAST.

WHEN THEY'D EATEN, JESUS TOOK SIMON PETER ON ONE SIDE, AND ASKED HIM THE SAME QUESTION THREE TIMES:

AND THREE TIMES PETER GAVE THE SAME ANSWER.

SIMON, DO YOU LOVE ME?

LORD, YOU KNOW EVERYTHING. YOU KNOW I LOVE YOU.

THEN FEED MY SHEEP.

13

I WONDER WHAT'S GOING TO HAPPEN. HE SENDS US OUT, BUT AT THE SAME TIME HE STAYS WITH US...

YOU KNOW IT'S DIFFICULT FOR US TO UNDERSTAND...

BUT, PETER, WHY DID THE MASTER SAY WE MUST GO BACK TO JERUSALEM?

BECAUSE THE FEAST OF SHAVUOT IS COMING, AND WE MUST GO TO JERUSALEM FOR IT.

* Pentecost, 50 days after Passover.

A LITTLE WHILE LATER...

WE'LL LEAVE EARLY TOMORROW, AND GO THROUGH THE JORDAN VALLEY.

JEWS FROM EVERY COUNTRY WENT UP TO JERUSALEM TO CELEBRATE THE GIVING OF THE TORAH TO MOSES.

NOT FAR FROM THE HOLY CITY...

FOLLOW ME YOUR MASTER WAITING FOR

...ER JESUS HAD ASCENDED ...HEAVEN, PETER TURNED TO ...BROTHER-DISCIPLES.

LET'S DO AS THE MASTER SAID, AND GO BACK TO THE UPPER ROOM.

...E DISCIPLES AND ..., JESUS' MOTHER, ...RED IN THE ... ROOM.

LET'S PRAY AND GET READY TO RECEIVE WHAT THE LORD PROMISED US.

GATHERED AROUND PETER, THE DISCIPLES SPENT SEVERAL DAYS PRAYING AND FASTING.

BROTHERS, JUDAS WAS ONE OF US AND SHARED OUR WORK, BEFORE HE BETRAYED JESUS. NOW SOMEBODY MUST TAKE HIS PLACE...

...ONE WHO'S BEEN WITH US FROM THE BEGINNING.

WE PROPOSE JOSEPH JUSTUS...

...AND WE PROPOSE MATTHIAS.

LORD, YOU KNOW OUR THOUGHTS; SHOW US WHOM YOU CHOOSE.

JOSEPH!

MATTHIAS!

IT'S MATTHIAS!

MATTHIAS, FROM NOW ON YOU SHARE IN THIS WORK WHICH JUDAS ABANDONED.

THE DAY OF THE PENTECOST WAS DRAWING NEAR. GREAT CROWDS OF PILGRIMS FLOCKED TO JERUSALEM FROM NORTH, SOUTH, EAST AND WEST.

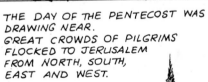

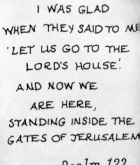

I WAS GLAD WHEN THEY SAID TO ME 'LET US GO TO THE LORD'S HOUSE.' AND NOW WE ARE HERE, STANDING INSIDE THE GATES OF JERUSALEM

- Psalm 122

19

THEN PETER SPOKE.

LISTEN TO ME, ALL OF YOU! SOME PEOPLE SAY WE'RE DRUNK. BE SERIOUS: IT'S ONLY THE THIRD HOUR*...

* 9 o'clock a.m.

REMEMBER WHAT THE PROPHET JOEL SAID: IN THE LAST DAYS I WILL POUR OUT MY SPIRIT ON EVERYONE...

...YOUR SONS AND DAUGHTERS WILL HAVE VISIONS; YOUR OLD MEN WILL DREAM DREAMS...'

WELL, I'M TELLING YOU THAT THIS PROPHECY'S BEING FULFILLED TODAY.

AND JOHN ADDED...

KNOW THIS, BROTHERS: JESUS OF NAZARETH, WHO WAS CRUCIFIED, HAS REALLY RISEN FROM THE DEAD!

DAVID WAS TALKING ABOUT HIM WHEN HE SAID: 'YOU WILL NOT LEAVE ME IN THE WORLD OF THE DEAD'.

AND JAMES...

YES, THIS JESUS IS ALIVE, AND WE'RE THE WITNESSES! HE'S THE CHRIST YOU CRUCIFIED!

MANY IN THE CROWD WERE DEEPLY TROUBLED BY WHAT THEY HEARD.

THESE MEN ARE TELLING THE TRUTH. YOU CAN SEE BY THEIR FACES!

YOU'RE RIGHT; THEY'RE MEN OF GOD.

AND PETER REPLIED...

BROTHERS, WHAT MUST WE DO?

EACH OF YOU MUST TURN TO GOD, BE BAPTIZED THE NAME OF JESUS CHRIST, AND THEN YOU TOO WILL RECEI THE HOLY SPIRIT.

JOHN, IN HIS

JOHN THE BAPTIST SAID, 'I BAPTIZE YOU WITH WATER, BUT THE ONE WHO COMES AFTER ME WILL BAPTIZE YOU WITH THE HOLY SPIRIT.'

25

IN FRONT OF YOU ALL, WHO ARE HIS DISCIPLES, I ACKNOWLEDGE THAT JESUS OF NAZARETH IS TRULY THE MESSIAH FORETOLD BY THE PROPHETS.

EVERY DAY MANY CONVERTS JOINED PETER AND THE OTHER APOSTLES.

SCENARIO: Etienne DAHLER
DRAWING: Carlo MARCELLO

PETER AND THE JERUSALEM CHURCH

BE BAPTIZED IN THE NAME OF JESUS CHRIST, AND YOU'LL BECOME PART OF OUR COMMUNITY.

THE WORD 'COMMUNITY'* WAS OFTEN USED TO DESCRIBE JESUS' DISCIPLES, BECAUSE THEY MET TOGETHER SO REGULARLY.
* In Greek, ekklesia, meaning 'assembly' and so 'church'.

OVER THERE... ISN'T THAT THE BEGGAR FROM THE BEAUTIFUL GATE?

IT CERTAINLY IS, BUT HE'S WALKING!

UNBELIEVABLE! LET'S GO AND SEE!

PETER, EVERYBODY'S FOLLOWING US. YOU MUST SPEAK TO THEM.

FELLOW ISRAELITES, WHY ARE YOU SURPRISED AT THIS? DO YOU THINK IT WAS BY OUR OWN POWER THAT WE MADE THIS MAN WALK?

KNOW THAT JESUS OF NAZARETH, WHOM YOU HANDED OVER TO BE KILLED, WAS RAISED BY THE GOD OF OUR FATHERS.

WHAT DO YOU MEAN?

IT'S TRUE; WE'RE THE WITNESSES...

THIS MAN'S BEEN HEALED IN THE NAME OF JESUS!

THAT'S RIGHT!

TURN BACK TO GOD! BECAUSE IT WAS FIRST OF ALL FOR YOU THAT HE SENT HIS SERVANT.

YOU'D BETTER GO AND ALERT THE COMMANDER OF THE TEMPLE GUARD, BEFORE THESE TWO CAUSE ANY TROUBLE.

RIGHT!

HE EVEN SAID THAT JESUS IS ALIVE AND STILL DOING THINGS.

IT'S MORE THAN ENOUGH TO HAVE THEM ARRESTED!

MOSHE, ASSEMBLE THE GUARD!

AT THE HOUSE OF THE COMMANDER OF THE TEMPLE GUARD.

MAKE WAY!

THAT'S ENOUGH! I'M ARRESTING YOU!

MANY OF THOSE WHO WERE THERE BELIEVED IN JESUS AND JOINED THE APOSTLES.

THE NEXT MORNING PETER AND JOHN APPEARED BEFORE THE SANHEDRIN. CAIAPHAS QUESTIONED THEM.

BY WHOSE POWER OR IN WHOSE NAME DID YOU DO THIS?

IN THE NAME OF JESUS CHRIST OF NAZARETH, WHOM YOU CRUCIFIED AND GOD RAISED FROM THE DEAD.

HE'S THE STONE YOU BUILDERS THREW AWAY, BUT NOW IT'S BECOME THE MOST IMPORTANT OF ALL!

TAKE THE ACCUSED OUTSIDE

THEY'RE SO SURE OF THEMSELVES— THAT'S WHAT BOTHERS ME.

AND EVERYBODY KNOWS THERE'S BEEN A MIRACLE!

WE MUST DO A WE CAN TO KE THIS FROM SPRE ANY FURTHER AMONG THE PEOPLE.

S AND HIS WIFE SAPPHIRA HAD
LLY AGREED TO HIDE PART OF THE
. ABOUT 3 HOURS LATER SAPPHIRA
TO PETER.

YOUR HUSBAND
UGHT US THIS MONEY.
T THE FULL AMOUNT
GOT FOR SELLING
YOUR FIELD?

THAT'S
RIGHT; IT'S
ALL THERE.

YOU BOTH PLOTTED TO DECEIVE
THE LORD! THE MEN WHO
BURIED YOUR HUSBAND
WILL CARRY YOU OUT
TOO!

THE MASTER
SAID THAT ALL SINS
WILL BE FORGIVEN,
BUT THOSE
WHO SIN AGAINST
THE HOLY SPIRIT
WON'T BE FORGIVEN.

THE WHOLE CHURCH AND ALL
OTHERS WHO HEARD WHAT HAD
HAPPENED WERE VERY AFRAID.

EVERY DAY THE
APOSTLES BECAME
MORE FAMOUS.

LORD,
HAVE MERCY ON
OUR SICK BROTHER!

I CAN SEE!
I CAN SEE!

PETER AND THE OTHER
APOSTLES AGAIN BEGAN TO
SPEAK BOLDLY IN THE
TEMPLE PORCH.

IT'S JESUS WHO
HEALS, HE WHO
SAVES YOU!

DON'T TAKE ANY FURTHER ACTION AGAINST THESE MEN. IF WHAT THEY'RE SAYING AND DOING IS ONLY SOMETHING HUMAN, IT WILL COME TO NOTHING...

...BUT IF IT COMES FROM GOD, YOU'LL NEVER DESTROY IT... TAKE CARE THAT YOU DON'T FIND YOURSELVES FIGHTING AGAINST GOD!

RABBI GAMALIEL, YOU'VE SAID A WISE THING. I AGREE.

SO DO I!

AND I

GOOD! BRING BACK THE ACCUSE

YOU'RE CONDEMNED TO BE WHIPPED... AND – FOR THE LAST TIME – WE ORDER YOU NEVER AGAIN TO SPEAK IN THE NAME OF JESUS.

AFTER THE WHIPPING, THE APOSTLES WERE SET FREE.

THIS TIME THEY WERE SHAKEN. I THINK THEY'LL LEAVE US IN PEACE.

THE APOSTLES WEN ON PREACHING THE GOOD NEWS ABOUT JESUS CHRIST WITH EVEN MORE VIGOUR.

NUMBER OF CONVERTS
PT GROWING...
CH CAUSED
TAIN PROBLEMS...

THIS CAN'T GO ON! I MUST TALK TO PETER!

QUITE SO! HERE HE IS...

WELL, WHAT'S GOING ON?

PETER, WHEN THE SUPPLIES ARE HANDED OUT EACH DAY, THE WIDOWS OF THE HELLENES* ARE BEING NEGLECTED.

* Greek-speaking Jews.

PETER CALLED THE APOSTLES TOGETHER...

I THINK WE SHOULD STICK TO THE PREACHING.

WE CAN'T DO EVERYTHING OURSELVES OR BE EVERYWHERE AT ONCE!

I AGREE. I SUGGEST THAT THE MEETING CHOOSES 7 BROTHERS WHO'LL BE IN CHARGE OF SERVING THE TABLES.

UST ADMIT THAT ALL E IN CHARGE OF SERVING HE TABLES ARE REWS*, AND SOMETIMES OPLE AREN'T TREATED FAIRLY...

WE MUST ORGANIZE THINGS DIFFERENTLY, SO THAT THAT DOESN'T HAPPEN AGAIN.

stinian Jews, speaking Aramaic.

HERE ARE THE 7 BROTHERS WHO WERE ELECTED: STEPHEN, PHILIP, PROCHORUS, TIMON, PARMENAS AND NICOLAUS.

THE APOSTLES AGREED WITH THE MEN CHOSEN BY THE MEETING, AND LAID HANDS ON THEM.

BE LIKE THE MASTER, WHO DIDN'T COME TO BE SERVED, BUT TO SERVE.

EACH DAY MORE AND MORE PEOPLE BECAME DISCIPLES.

WE'RE A GROUP OF LEVITES; WE WANT TO BE BAPTIZED.

YES, WE BELIEVE THAT JESUS IS THE MESSIAH.

SOON A YOUNG RABBI, A COUNCILLOR OF THE SANHEDRIN, WENT TO CAIAPHAS, THE HIGH PRIEST.

THE NAZARENES ARE A REAL THREAT TO OUR RELIGION. HOW CAN YOU ALLOW THEM TO ACT FREELY?

WE FOLLOWED GAMALIEL'S ADVICE. NO DOUBT WE WERE WRONG!

ARREST THEIR LEADERS AND PUT THEM TO DEATH!

EVERYBODY CAN SEE THAT THIS MOVEMENT'S BEEN ALLOWED TO LAST TOO LONG!

AND... WHAT EXACTLY DO YOU SUGGEST, **SAUL OF TARSUS**?

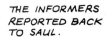
THE INFORMERS REPORTED BACK TO SAUL.

THAT STEPHEN'S A TROUBLE-MAKER. EVERYONE LISTENS TO HIM AS IF HE'S AN EXPERT.

A FEW DAYS LATER, WHILE STEPHEN WAS PREACHING IN THE SYNAGOGUE...

HE SHOULD SHUT UP! THAT MAN'S BLASPHEMING AGAINST MOSES AND GOD!

THAT JESUS WAS NOTHING BUT A DECEIVER, A BANDIT!

NO, LET HIM SPEAK!

PERFECT! I'LL DEAL WITH IT!

TAKE YOUR HANDS OFF THIS UPRIGHT MAN!

AN UPRIGHT MAN? WHO BETRAYS THE LAW AND THE PROPHETS?

SEIZE HIM, AND TAKE HIM BEFORE THE SANHEDRIN!

THE REST OF YOU GO HOME, IF YOU DON'T WANT THE SAME TO HAPPEN TO YOU!

VERY SOON, BEFORE THE SANHEDRIN, IN THE PRESENCE OF CAIAPHAS...

LET THE TRIAL BEGIN! BRING IN THE WITNESSES...

CAIAPHAS READ THE COURT'S SENTENCE...

BEING FOUND GUILTY OF BLASPHEMY AND OF LEADING THE ISRAELITES ASTRAY FROM THE RIGHT PATH, STEPHEN IS CONDEMNED TO BE STONED TO DEATH.

THEY TOOK STEPHEN TO THE PLACE OF STONING.

THROW HIM IN!

YOU HERETIC! YOU'RE WORSE THAN A PAGAN!

YOU'LL GO STRAIGHT TO THE FIRES OF GEHENNAH!

MAKE WAY!

LORD JESUS, RECEIVE MY SPIRIT.

LET THE WITNESSES THROW THE FIRST STONES.

LORD, DON'T HOLD THIS SIN AGAINST THEM!

AND NOW LET THE OTHER PEOPLE COME FORWARD.

THE HARVEST'S GREAT! MANY HEARTS ARE OPENING TO THE LORD!

THAT SAME EVENING PETER PRAYED...

LORD, SEND YOUR SPIRIT, AS YOU PROMISED, TO ACT POWERFULLY AMONG OUR BROTHERS.

PETER AND JOHN STAYED IN SAMARIA FOR A WHILE, PREACHING ABOUT JESUS CHRIST THE SAVIOUR, AND HEALING THE SICK. THEN THEY WENT BACK TO JERUSALEM.

THIS IS WHAT HAPPENED NEXT TO PHILIP, ONE OF THE 7 DEACONS.

WHEN HE REACHED THAT ROAD...

IT'S VERY STRANGE! THE JEWS REJECT THE MESSIAH, AND THE SAMARITANS WELCOME HIM!

JOHN, I BELIEVE THIS IS ONLY THE FIRST OF MANY SURPRISES...

GET UP, PHILIP, AND GO SOUTH TO THE ROAD BETWEEN JERUSALEM AND GAZA!

GO AND MEET THAT CHARIOT.

PHILIP GOT UP STRAIGHT AWAY AND WENT.